CW01085192

JONATHAN SWIFT

Gulliver
in
Lilliput

Retold by María José Lobo
and Pepita Subirà

MACMILLAN

Picture Glossary

sea

storm

wave

ship

beach

bow

arrow

horse

temple

tree

mountain

garden

emperor

officer

pocket

egg

It is 4th May, 1699. The Antelope is going to the Far East.

My name's Lemuel Gulliver. I'm a ship's doctor. I like travelling. I'm going to the East Indies.

One night the sea is rough.

What's wrong?

Help!

It's a storm!

There are a lot of waves. The ship and the other men disappear under the water. Gulliver swims and swims.

Finally, Gulliver arrives at a beach. He cannot see any houses. He is very tired and he goes to sleep.

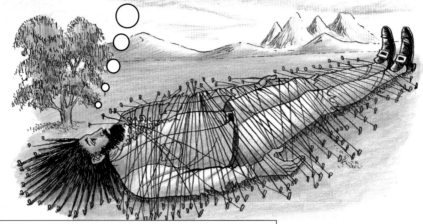

There is something on Gulliver's hand.
It is moving up his arm.

Gulliver opens his eyes. He sees a very little man.

5

The man is about 15 centimetres tall. He is looking at Gulliver. Gulliver is very surprised.

Gulliver says 'Hello' to the little man. The little man runs away!

Hello!

There are hundreds of little men. They have got bows and arrows. They speak a strange language.

Gulliver is very hungry. He is very thirsty too.

But the little men do not understand Gulliver. He moves his hand up and down. Finally, his hand is free. He points to his mouth.

Now the little men understand. They give Gulliver meat, bread, fruit and milk. Gulliver is happy.

Gulliver goes to sleep again. The little men take him to the city. They need more than 1000 horses!

Gulliver wakes up. He is next to a big temple. He cannot escape.

Gulliver stands up. He can see a city, trees and mountains. Everything is very small.

One day the emperor visits Gulliver. He speaks to Gulliver, but Gulliver does not understand the emperor.

The emperor sends ten clever teachers. They teach Gulliver their language. Gulliver learns very quickly. The country's name is Lilliput. The language is called Lilliputian. Gulliver is very happy. Now he can talk to the little people.

One day Gulliver asks the emperor a question.

Please, your majesty, can I go? I want to be free!

But the emperor is not sure. 'Is Gulliver dangerous?' he thinks. The emperor asks some officers to look in Gulliver's pockets. Gulliver helps the men. The officers make a list of the things they find.

They tell the emperor what is in Gulliver's pockets.

This strange thing is for his hair.

This machine says 'tick tock'.

This is a book. But we don't understand the words.

We don't know what this is.

Fine. You can free Gulliver.

Gulliver is free now. He visits the city. The children play with him in the streets. Gulliver is very happy.

One day the emperor talks to Gulliver.

We need your help. The people of Blefuscu want to attack Lilliput.

What's Blefuscu?

It's a country. The people of Blefuscu are bad.

Why do they want to attack Lilliput?

... they eat their eggs like that.

Oh! And is that important?

Because we eat our eggs like this and ...

Very important.

Really?

Gulliver helps the emperor.
He goes to Blefuscu and pulls its ships to Lilliput.
Now Blefuscu cannot attack Lilliput.

The emperor of Lilliput is very happy. But there are some bad men in Lilliput. They want to kill Gulliver. 'He is too big. He eats too much,' say the bad men.

So one day Gulliver leaves Lilliput. He goes to Blefuscu and looks for new adventures there.